Chart HITS NOW 1

Published by
Wise Publications
14-15 Berners Street, London W1T 3LJ, UK.

Exclusive Distributors:
Music Sales Limited
Distribution Centre, Newmarket Road, Bury St Edmunds, Suffolk IP33 3YB, UK.
Music Sales Corporation
180 Madison Avenue, 24th Floor, New York NY 10016, USA.
Music Sales Pty Limited
4th floor, Lisgar House, 30-32 Carrington Street, Sydney, NSW 2000, Australia.

Order No. AM1011813
ISBN 978-1-78558-291-2
This book © Copyright 2016 Wise Publications, a division of Music Sales Limited.

Compiled & edited by Naomi Gibb, sub-edited by Lisa Cox.
Music arranged by Alistair Watson & Matt Cowe.
Music processed by Sarah Lofthouse, SEL Music Art Limited.
Cover designed by Michael Bell Design.
Printed in the EU.

www.musicsales.com

WISE PUBLICATIONS
part of The Music Sales Group
London / New York / Paris / Sydney / Copenhagen / Berlin / Madrid / Hong Kong / Tokyo

Chart HITS NOW 1

■ **EASY PIANO**

Chart HITS NOW 1

■ **LYRICS & GUITAR CHORD BOXES**

The Grand Staff

Music for the piano or keyboard is usually written on a **grand staff** — two staves joined by a **brace**.

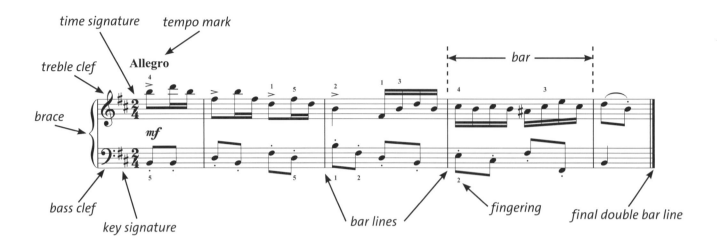

Notes on the upper stave, headed by the **treble clef** (or *G clef*), are usually played by the right hand.

Notes on the lower stave, headed by the **bass clef** (or *F clef*), are usually played by the left hand.

The music is divided by **bar lines** into **bars**. Usually, each bar contains the same number of beats (counts), as indicated by the **time signature** at the beginning of the music.

Notes values and rests

The note value tells you the duration of a note — how many beats it lasts. When read in sequence, note values show the rhythm of the music.

Each has its own rest, which indicates a silence for the equivalent duration.

symbol	name	duration	rest
semibreve	semibreve	4 beats	—
𝅗𝅥 or	minim	2 beats	—
𝅘𝅥 or	crotchet	1 beat	𝄽
𝅘𝅥𝅮 or	quaver	½ beat	𝄾
𝅘𝅥𝅯 or	semiquaver	¼ beat	𝄿

Clefs

The right hand usually plays music written in the **treble clef**.

This is also called the *G clef* because it spirals around the line on which the note G above Middle C is written.

The left hand usually plays music written in the **bass clef**.

This is also called the *F clef* because there are two dots either side of the line on which the note F below Middle C is written.

Sharps, flats and naturals

♯ A **sharp** sign raises the pitch of a note by a semitone to the very next key on the right.

♭ A **flat** sign lowers the pitch of a note by a semitone to the very next key on the left.

♮ A **natural** sign cancels the effect of a sharp or a flat, representing the unaltered pitch.

A **key signature** is written at the start of each line of music. It tells us which notes should be played as *sharps* or *flats* and saves writing a ♯ or ♭ sign every time these notes appear.

Time signatures

The **time signature** appears after the key signature at the beginning of the music.

The *upper figure* shows the number of beats in each bar and the *lower figure* tells us what note duration gets one beat.

4/4 *or* **C** = four crotchet beats per bar
(also called common time)

3/4 = three crotchet beats per bar

2/4 = two crotchet beats per bar

2/2 *or* **₵** = two minim beats per bar
(also called cut common time)

6/8 = six quaver beats per bar

12/8 = twelve quaver beats per bar

Other musical signs

‖ A **double bar line** marks the beginning of a new section of music.

‖ A **final double bar line** marks the end of a piece.

A **slur** is a curved line, over or under a group of notes, indicating that they should be played smoothly (*legato*).

A **tie** is a curved line, connecting two consecutive notes of the same pitch — only the first should be played and then held for the combined value of both notes.

A **staccato** dot, above or below a note, indicates that the note should be played as short and detached.

An **accent** mark, above or below a note, indicates that it should be emphasized by playing it louder than the general dynamic.

A **fermata** (or **pause**) indicates that the note should be held for longer than its written duration.

Fingering numbers

Your fingers are given numbers from 1 to 5, starting with the thumbs and numbering outwards.

Fingering is sometimes written above or below notes to help you move your hands around the keyboard efficiently.

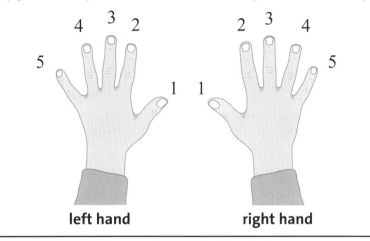

left hand   right hand

Dynamics

A **dynamic mark** tells you how loudly or softly to play.

pp	**pianissimo**	very soft
p	**piano**	soft
mp	**mezzo piano**	moderately soft
mf	**mezzo forte**	moderately loud
f	**forte**	loud
ff	**fortissimo**	very loud

crescendo *cresc.* gradually getting louder

diminuendo *dim.* gradually getting softer

Repeat signs and other navigation marks

:‖ This is an end **repeat sign**, which tells you to repeat back from the beginning, or from the start repeat: ‖:

|1. |2.   **First-** and **second-time bars** are used to indicate passages in a repeated section that are only performed on certain playings.

D.C. *(Da Capo)* tells you to repeat from the beginning.

D.C. al Fine *(Da Capo al Fine)* tells you to repeat from the beginning to the end, or up to **Fine**.

D.S. *(Dal Segno)* tells you to repeat from the sign 𝄋.

D.S. al Coda *(Dal Segno al Coda)* tells you to repeat from the sign 𝄋 and then, when you reach **to Coda** ⊕, you should jump to the Coda, marked ⊕ **Coda**.

Key signatures

The key of the music is indicated by the **key signature** at the start of each stave, just after the clef. It tells you which notes in the music should be played as *sharps* or *flats*.

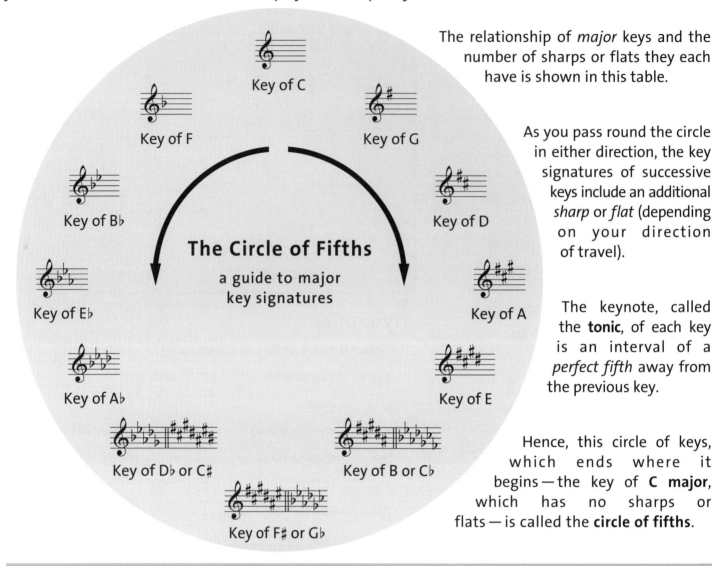

The relationship of *major* keys and the number of sharps or flats they each have is shown in this table.

As you pass round the circle in either direction, the key signatures of successive keys include an additional *sharp* or *flat* (depending on your direction of travel).

The keynote, called the **tonic**, of each key is an interval of a *perfect fifth* away from the previous key.

Hence, this circle of keys, which ends where it begins — the key of **C major**, which has no sharps or flats — is called the **circle of fifths**.

More about note values and rhythms

A **dotted note** lasts for 1½ times its usual duration.

symbol	name	duration	rest
𝅗𝅥. or ⌐·	dotted minim	3 beats	▬
♩. or ⌐·	dotted crotchet	1½ beats	𝄽·
♪. or ♪·	dotted quaver	¾ beat	𝄾·

A **triplet** is a subdivision of a beat or beats into three notes of equal duration. Using any note value as a unit, three *triplet* notes divide the duration that two notes would normally occupy into three.

Triplet quavers ♪♪♪ divide a crotchet (two quavers) into three

Triplet crotchets ♩♩♩ divide a minim (two crotchets) into three

A **beam** is often used to join note values of a *quaver* or shorter to show a rhythmic grouping.

The most common grouping is by *crotchet* beat, which can help you see where the beats of the bar fall.

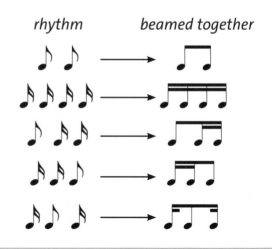

6

EYES SHUT

Words & Music by
Oliver Thornton / Michael Goldsworthy / Resul Turkmen

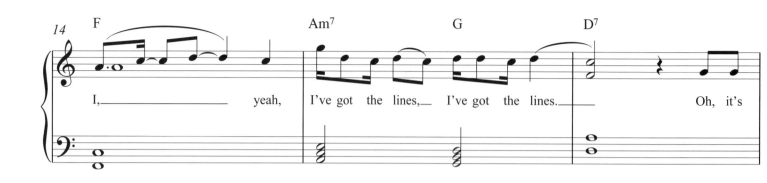

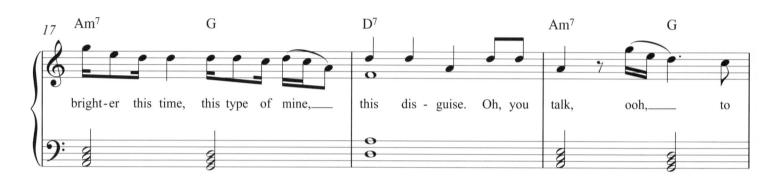

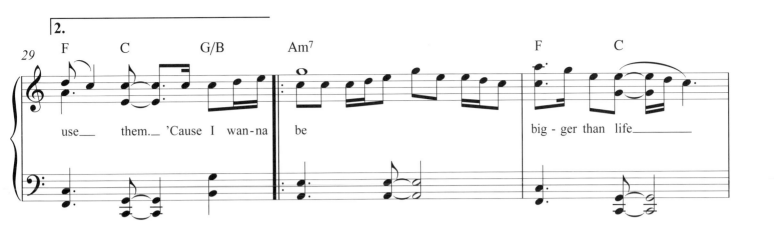

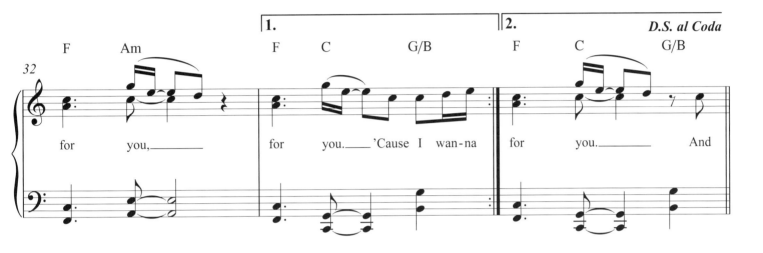

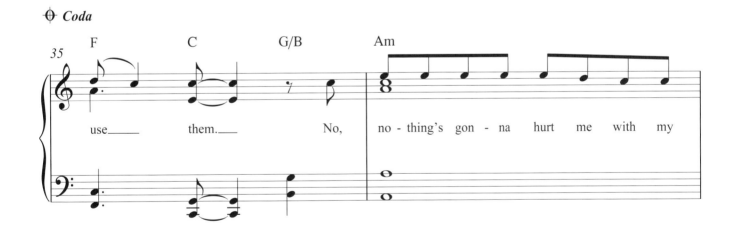

9

ADVENTURE OF A LIFETIME

Words & Music by
Guy Berryman / Chris Martin / Jon Buckland / Will Champion
Mikkel Eriksen / Tor Erik Hermansen

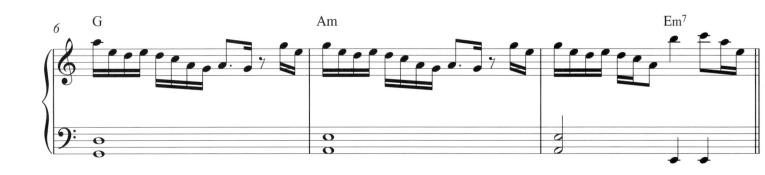

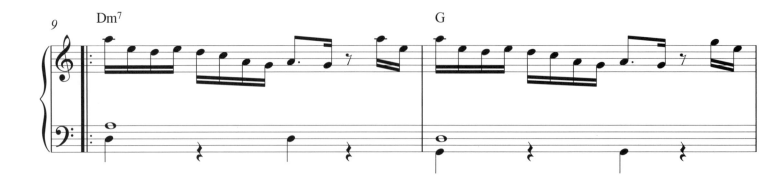

13

14

HELLO

Words & Music by
Greg Kurstin / Adele Adkins

19

LOVE YOURSELF

Words & Music by
Justin Bieber / Benny Blanco / Ed Sheeran

23

PILLOWTALK

Words & Music by
Zain Malik / Anthony Hannides / Michael Hannides
Joe Garrett / Levi Malundama

EYES SHUT

Words & Music by
Oliver Thornton / Michael Goldsworthy / Resul Turkmen

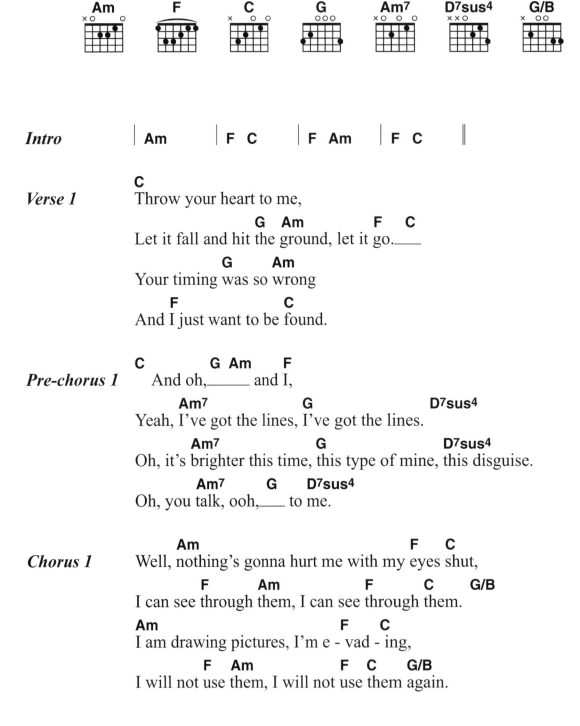

Intro | Am | F C | F Am | F C ‖

Verse 1

C
Throw your heart to me,

                 G Am   F C
Let it fall and hit the ground, let it go.____

            G   Am
Your timing was so wrong

      F   C
And I just want to be found.

Pre-chorus 1

C   G Am   F
And oh,_____ and I,

Am7   G   D7sus4
Yeah, I've got the lines, I've got the lines.

Am7   G   D7sus4
Oh, it's brighter this time, this type of mine, this disguise.

Am7   G   D7sus4
Oh, you talk, ooh,___ to me.

Chorus 1

           Am   F   C
Well, nothing's gonna hurt me with my eyes shut,

          F   Am   F   C   G/B
I can see through them, I can see through them.

Am   F   C
I am drawing pictures, I'm e - vad - ing,

           F   Am   F   C   G/B
I will not use them, I will not use them again.

Link | Am | F C | F Am | F C   ‖

Verse 2
         C
And it starts again,

                         G   Am
You come over with your friends,

 F   C
I don't wanna talk to them.

             G   Am F   C
And all I really want is to start a - gain.

Pre-chorus 2   As Pre-chorus 1

Chorus 2
           Am   F   C
Well, nothing's gonna hurt me with my eyes shut,

                 F   Am   F   C   G/B
I can see through them, I can see through them.

Am   F   C
I am drawing pictures, I'm e - vad - ing,

            F   Am   F   C
I will not use them, I will not use them.

Bridge
          G/B   Am7 F   C F Am F C
'Cause I wanna be   bigger than life for you, for you.

          G/B   Am7 F   C F Am F C   G/B
'Cause I wanna be   bigger than life for you, for you.

Chorus 3
           Am   F   C
And nothing's gonna hurt me with my eyes shut,

                 F   Am   F   C   G/B
I can see through them, I can see through them.

Am   F   C
I am drawing pictures, I'm e - vad - ing,

            F   Am   F   C   G/B
I will not use them, I will not use them.

     Am   F   C
No, nothing's gonna hurt me with my eyes shut,

               F   Am   F   C
I can see through them, I can see through them.

ADVENTURE OF A LIFETIME
Words & Music by
Guy Berryman / Chris Martin / Jon Buckland / Will Champion
Mikkel Eriksen / Tor Erik Hermansen

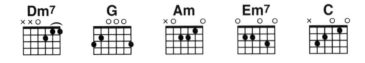

Dm⁷   G   Am   Em⁷   C

Intro

| (N.C.) | (N.C.) | (N.C.) | (N.C.) |

| Dm⁷ | G | Am | Am Em⁷ |

| Dm⁷ | G | Am | Am C G |

| Dm⁷ | G | Am | Am C G ‖

Verse 1

$\quad$ Dm⁷ $\qquad\qquad$ G $\qquad$ Am
$\quad$ Turn your magic on, Umi she'd say,

$\qquad\qquad\qquad\qquad\qquad$ C $\quad$ G $\quad$ Dm⁷
Everything you want's a dream away.

$\qquad$ G $\qquad\qquad$ Am
We are legends, every day,

$\qquad\qquad\qquad\qquad$ C G
That's what she told me.

Verse 2

$\quad$ Dm⁷ $\qquad\qquad$ G $\qquad$ Am
$\quad$ Turn your magic on, to me she'd say,

$\qquad\qquad\qquad\qquad\qquad$ C $\quad$ G $\quad$ Dm⁷
Everything you want's a dream away.

$\qquad$ G $\qquad\qquad$ Am
Under this pressure, under this weight

We are diamonds.

Chorus 1

        C G Dm⁷   **G**
Now I feel my heart beating,

        Am
I feel my heart underneath my skin.

        C G Dm⁷   **G**
Oh I can feel my heart beating,

             Am   **Em⁷**
Oh, you make me feel like I'm a - live again.

Dm⁷ **G** **Am**   **C** **G**   **Dm⁷ G**
         A - live again,

             Am   **C G**
Oh, you make me feel like I'm a - live again.

Verse 3

Dm⁷   **G**   **Am**
  Said I can't go on, not in this way,

               C   **G**   **Dm⁷**
I'm a dream that died by light of day.

          G   **Am**
Gonna hold up half the sky and say,

Only I own me.

Chorus 2   As Chorus 1

Link 1 | **Dm⁷** | **G** | **Am** | **Am G**   ‖

Verse 4

Dm⁷   **G**   **Am**
  Turn your magic on, Umi she'd say,

               G   **Dm⁷**
Everything you want's a dream away.

          G   **Am**
Under this pressure, under this weight

We are diamonds taking shape,

         Em⁷
We are diamonds taking shape.

Link 2

Dm⁷ **G** **Am**   **C G Dm⁷ G**   **Am**
        Woo,___   woo.___

Bridge

C G   Dm7   G
If we've only got this life,

       Am
This ad - venture, oh, then I...

     C   G Dm7   G
And if we've only got this life,

          Am
You get me through, ah.

     C   G Dm7   G
And if we've only got this life,

       Am
In this ad - venture, oh, then I

       C   G Dm7   G   Am
Want to share it with you, with you, with you.

             C
Sing it all, sing it, oh.

Outro

G   Dm7   G
Woo - hoo, (woohoo), woo - hoo, (woohoo),

     Am   C
Woo - hoo, (woohoo), woohoo, (woo - hoo).

G   Dm7   G
Woo - hoo, (woohoo), woo - hoo, (woohoo),

     Am   C
Woo - hoo, (woohoo), woohoo, (woo - hoo).

G   Dm7   G
Woo - hoo, (woohoo), woo - hoo, (woohoo),

     Am   N.C.
Woo - hoo, (woohoo), woo - hoo, (woohoo).

HELLO

Words & Music by
Greg Kurstin / Adele Adkins

Em   G   D   C

Capo first fret

Intro | Em G | D C ‖

Verse 1
     Em G   D C
Hel - lo,   it's me,_____
     Em   G   D   C
I was wondering if after all these years you'd like to meet
     Em G   D C
To go over every - thing.
          Em   G
They say that time's supposed to heal ya,
      D   C
But I ain't done much healing.

Verse 2
     Em G   D C
Hel - lo, can you hear me?
     Em   G   C   D
I'm in Califor - nia dreaming about who we used to be
        Em   G   C D
When we were younger and free.
       Em   G   C   D
I've forgot - ten how it felt before the world fell at our feet.
        Em   D   Bm C   Em D C
There's such a difference be - tween us and a mill - ion miles.

```
              Em         C              G  D
Chorus 1      Hello from the other side,_____
               Em          C              G  D
              I must've called a thousand times
                    Em   C          G          D
              To tell you I'm sorry for every - thing that I've done,
                       Em   C  G        D
              But when I call you never seem to be home.
              Em         C          G  D
              Hello from the outside,_____
                Em        C              G  D
              At least I can say that I've tried_____
                    Em   C    G          D
              To tell you I'm sorry for breaking your heart,
                               Em
              But it don't mat - ter,
                 C          G         D         Em     G D C
              It clearly doesn't tear you a - part any - more.


                    Em G      D       C
Verse 2       Hel - lo,     how are you?
                    Em    G          D          C
              It's so typical of me to talk a - bout myself, I'm sorry.
              Em  G       D    C
              I hope   that you're well.
                       Em        G              C       D
              Did you ever make it out of that town where nothing ever happened?
                       Em  D      Bm   C    Em    D   C
              It's no secret   that the both of us are running out of time.


                 Em        C          G  D
Chorus 2      So hello from the other side,_____
              Em              C            G  D
              I must have called a thousand times_____
                       Em   C         G          D
              To tell you I'm sorry for every - thing that I've done,
                       Em   C  G        D
              But when I call you never seem to be home.
              Em         C          G  D
              Hello from the outside,_____
                 Em        C              G  D
              At least I can say that I've tried_____
                       Em   C    G          D
              To tell you I'm sorry for breaking your heart,
                               Em  C          G         D       Em     C
              But it don't mat - ter, it clearly doesn't tear you a - part any - more.
```

34

Bridge

      D   **G**   **Em**   **C**
Ooh,___ any - more.

      D   **G**   **Em**   **C**
Ooh,___ any - more.

      D   **G**   **Em**   **C**
Ooh,___ any - more.

         D
Any - more.

Chorus 3

Em   **C**   **G D**
Hello from the other side,_____

 Em   **C**   **G D**
I must've called a thousand times____

        Em **C**   **G**   **D**
To tell you I'm sorry for every - thing that I've done,

             Em **C** **G**   **D**
But when I call you never seem to be home.

Em   **C**   **G D**
Hello from the outside,_____

  Em   **C**   **G D**
At least I can say that I've tried_____

        Em **C**   **G**   **D**
To tell you I'm sorry for breaking your heart,

               Em
But it don't mat - ter,

  C   **G**   **D**   **Em** **G D C Em**
It clearly doesn't tear you a - part any - more.

35

LOVE YOURSELF

Words & Music by
Justin Bieber / Benny Blanco / Ed Sheeran

E   B/D♯   C♯m   F♯m   C♯5   A5

E5   B5   E*   C♯m*   A   B7sus4

Capo first fret

Verse 1

N.C.   E   B/D♯   C♯m
For all the times that you rain on my pa - rade,

N.C.   F♯m   E   B/D♯
And all the clubs you get in using my name,

N.C.   E   B/D♯   C♯m
You think you broke my heart, oh girl, for goodness   sake,

N.C.   F♯m   E   B/D♯
You think I'm crying on my own, well I ain't.

Verse 2

N.C.   E
And I didn't wanna write a song

B/D♯   C♯m   N.C.   F♯m
  'Cause I didn't want anyone thinking I still care, I don't,

      E   B/D♯
But you still hit my phone up.

N.C.   E   B/D♯
And baby, I be movin' on

           C♯m   N.C.   F♯m
And I think you should be somethin' I don't wanna hold back,

E   B/D♯
Maybe you should know that.

Pre-chorus 1

N.C.   C♯5   A5   E5
My mama don't like you and she likes every - one

N.C.   C♯5   A5   E5
And I never like to admit that I was wrong

          C♯5   A5   E5   B5
And I've been so caught up in my job, didn't see what's go - ing on,

     C♯5 A5   B5
But now I know   I'm better sleeping on my own.

Chorus 1

N.C.	E*	B5	C#m*

'Cause if you like the way you look that much,

A	E*		B7sus4 E*

Oh baby, you should go and love your - self.

	E*	B5	C#m*	A

And if you think that I'm still holding on to somethin',

E*		B7sus4 E*

You should go and love your - self.

Verse 3

N.C.	E	B/D#	C#m

But when you told me that you hated my friends,

N.C.	F#m	E	B/D#

The only problem was with you and not them;

N.C.	E	B/D#	C#m

And every time you told me my opinion was wrong

N.C.	F#m	E	B/D#

And tried to make me forget where I came from.

Verse 4   As Verse 2

Pre-chorus 2   As Pre-chorus 1

Chorus 2   As Chorus 1

Instr.   ‖: E* B5 | C#m A | E* B7sus4 | E*   :‖

Verse 5

N.C.	E	B/D#	C#m

For all the times that you made me feel small,

N.C.	F#m	E	B/D#

I fell in love, now I feel nothin' at all.

N.C.	E	B/D#	C#m

Had never felt so low when I was vuln'ra - ble,

N.C.	F#m	E	B/D#

Was I a fool to let you break down my walls?

Chorus 3   As Chorus 1

Chorus 4   As Chorus 1

PILLOWTALK

Words & Music by
Zain Malik / Anthony Hannides / Michael Hannides
Joe Garrett / Levi Malundama

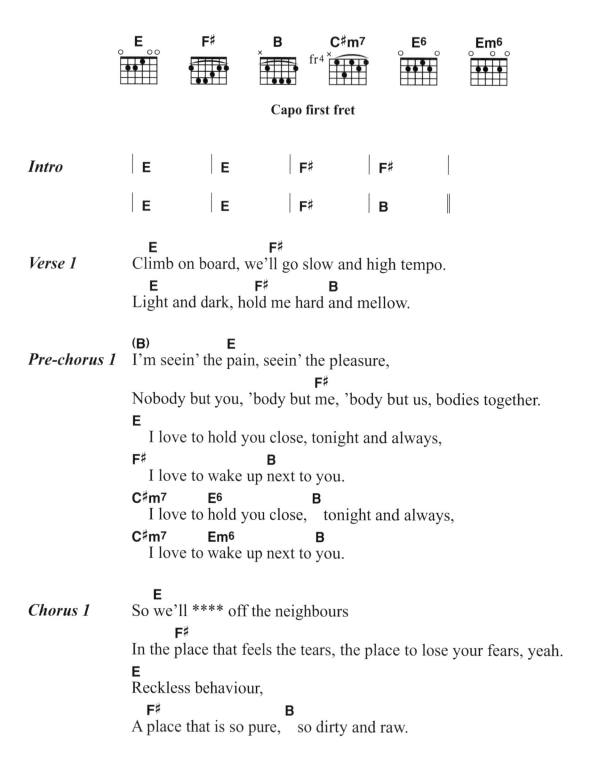

Capo first fret

Intro

| E | E | F♯ | F♯ |

| E | E | F♯ | B |

Verse 1

    E   F♯
Climb on board, we'll go slow and high tempo.
    E   F♯   B
Light and dark, hold me hard and mellow.

Pre-chorus 1

(B)   E
I'm seein' the pain, seein' the pleasure,
                   F♯
Nobody but you, 'body but me, 'body but us, bodies together.
E
   I love to hold you close, tonight and always,
F♯   B
   I love to wake up next to you.
C♯m7   E6   B
   I love to hold you close,   tonight and always,
C♯m7   Em6   B
   I love to wake up next to you.

Chorus 1

      E
So we'll **** off the neighbours
     F♯
In the place that feels the tears, the place to lose your fears, yeah.
E
Reckless behaviour,
   F♯   B
A place that is so pure,   so dirty and raw.

                         E
cont.   Be in the bed all day, bed all day, bed all day,

                        F♯
           Lovin' in, fighting on,

                                   E
           It's a paradise   and it's a war zone,

                  F♯   **B**
           It's a paradise   and it's a war zone.

                        E   **F♯**
Verse 2   Pillow talk, my enemy, my ally.

                        E   **F♯**   **B**
           Prisoners, then we're free, it's a thin line.

                       (B)   **E**
Pre-chorus 2   I'm seein' the pain, seein' the pleasure,

                                            F♯
           Nobody but you, 'body but me, 'body but us, bodies together.

                       E
             I love to hold you close, tonight and always,

                  F♯   **B**
             I love to wake up next to you.

Chorus 2   As Chorus 1

                       E
Bridge   Paradise, paradise, paradise, paradise,

                       F♯
           War zone, war zone, war zone, war zone.

                       E
           Paradise, paradise, paradise, paradise,

                       F♯   **B**
           War zone, war zone, war zone, war zone.

Interlude | **C♯m⁷ E⁶** | **B** | **C♯m⁷ Em⁶** | **B**   ‖

Chorus 3   As Chorus 1

1 2 3 4 5 6 7 8 9

Whatever you want...

Music Sales publishes the very best in printed music for rock & pop, film music, jazz, blues, country and classical as well as songs from all the great stage musicals.

Many of our practical publications come with helpful CDs or exclusive download links to music files for backing tracks and other audio extras.

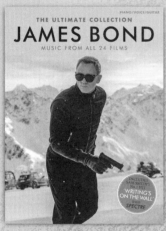

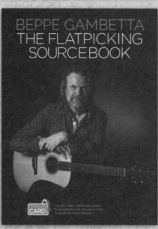

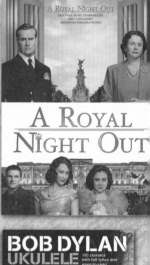

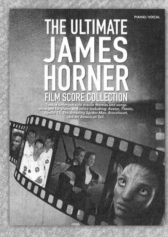

We also publish a range of tuition titles, books for audition use and book+DVD master classes that let you learn from the world's greatest performers.

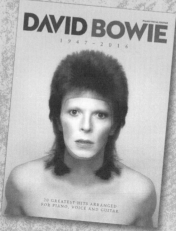

So, whatever you want, Music Sales has it.

Just visit your local music shop and ask to see our huge range of music in pr

In case of difficulty, contac marketing@musicsales.co